SRA Art Connections

Vocabulary

English and Spanish

Level 5

SRA McGraw-Hill

Columbus, Ohio

A Division of The McGraw·Hill Companies

Cover: Katsushika Hokusai. (Japanese). *The Great Wave off Kanagawa, 36 Views of Mount Fugi.* 1831–33. Polychrome woodblock print. 10 $\frac{1}{8}$ x 14 $\frac{15}{16}$ inches. Metropolitan Museum of Art, New York, New York.

SRA/McGraw-Hill

A Division of The McGraw·Hill Companies

Send all inquiries to:
SRA/McGraw-Hill
250 Old Wilson Bridge Road
Suite 310
Worthington, OH 43085

Printed in the United States of America.

ISBN 0-02-688331-7

1 2 3 4 5 6 7 8 9 DBH 01 00 99 98 97

Table of Contents

Name _____   Date _____

Lines

Vocabulary Words

curved	diagonal	horizontal
line	vertical	zigzag

A. Label each picture of a line with the correct vocabulary word.

1.   _____

2.   _____

3.   _____

4.   _____

5.   _____

B. In each sentence, circle the word that is another form of a vocabulary word.

   1. Perimeter is a kind of linear measurement.

   2. My dog can jump five feet vertically.

   3. The horizon stretches out straight and far.

C. Complete the paragraph with vocabulary words.

The pole-vaulter races down the track. The _____ lines on his uniform look like a lightning bolt. The bar forms a _____ line high in the air. It is held up by two metal poles that form _____ lines. The vaulter uses the pole to push himself into the air. It bends into a _____ line with his weight. Then it straightens and propels him up and over the bar.

Nombre _____   Fecha _____

Líneas

Palabras de vocabulario

curva	diagonal	horizontal
línea	vertical	en zigzag

A. Rotula cada dibujo de una línea con la palabra correcta de vocabulario.

1. _____

2. _____

3. _____

4. _____

5. _____

B. En cada oración, encierra en un círculo la palabra que represente una de las palabras del vocabulario.

1. El perímetro es un tipo de medida lineal.

2. Mi perro puede saltar cinco pies verticalmente.

3. El horizonte se extiende rectamente y hacia lo lejos.

C. Completa el párrafo con palabras de vocabulario.

El atleta del salto con garrocha corre por la pista. Las líneas

_____ de su uniforme parecen un relámpago. La

barra forma una línea _____ en el aire. Es sostenida

por dos postes de metal que forman líneas _____. El

atleta usa la vara para impulsarse en el aire. Se dobla

formando una línea _____ con su peso. Luego se

estira y se eleva pasando por encima de la barra.

Name _____   Date _____

Geometric and Free-Form Shapes

Vocabulary Words

complex geometric shape   free-form shape
geometric shape   shape

Complete the sentences with vocabulary words.

1. A drawing of clouds would probably use a

_____.

2. A _____ has length

and height but not depth.

3. A star made using triangles and a pentagon is a

_____.

4. A square is a _____.

Group the following shapes on the chart.

parallelogram   square   pentagon   circle   trapezoid
triangle   rectangle   hexagon   octagon   oval

Geometric Shapes	Complex Geometric Shapes
_____	_____
_____	_____
_____	_____
_____	_____

Nombre _____   Fecha _____

Figuras geométricas y abstractas

Palabras de vocabulario

figura geométrica compleja	figura abstracta
figura geométrica	figura

Completa las oraciones con palabras del vocabulario.

1. Para un dibujo de las nubes probablemente se usaría una

_____.

2. Una _____ tiene longitud y
altura pero no posee profundidad.

3. Una estrella que se hace con triángulos y un pentágono

es una _____.

4. Un cuadrado es una _____.

Agrupa las siguientes figuras en el cuadro.

paralelogramo   cuadrado   pentágono   círculo   trapecio
triángulo   rectángulo   hexágono   octágono   óvalo

Figuras geométricas	Figuras geométricas complejas
_____	_____
_____	_____
_____	_____
_____	_____

Name _____   Date _____

Value in Shading

Vocabulary Words

gradation   point of view
shading   value

A. In each blank, write the vocabulary word that fits.

    1. From this _____, his left cheek is in
shadow, but from that one, it is not.

    2. She added white paint to blue paint to lighten the
_____ of the color.

    3. The value scale goes from white to black through
_____ of gray.

    4. See how the artist has used _____ to
give the apple depth.

B. Write the vocabulary word that fits in each group.

    1. perspective, vantage point _____

    2. changes values _____

    3. shadow, marking _____

    4. brightness, darkness _____

C. Write four sentences. Use one vocabulary word in each
sentence.

_____

_____

_____

_____

Nombre _____ Fecha _____

El valor en el sombreado

Palabras de vocabulario

degradaciones   punto de vista

sombreado   valor

A. En cada espacio en blanco, escribe la palabra de vocabulario correspondiente.

  1. Desde este _____, su mejilla izquierda se ve sombreada, pero desde éste, no se ve sombreada.

  2. Ella le agregó pintura blanca a la azul para aclarar el _____ del color.

  3. La escala del valor se extiende desde blanco hasta negro a través de _____ de gris.

  4. Fíjate cómo el artista usa el _____ para darle profundidad a la manzana.

B. Escribe la palabra de vocabulario que corresponde a cada grupo.

  1. perspectiva, posición ventajosa _____

  2. cambia el valor _____

  3. sombra, marcas _____

  4. brillo, oscuridad _____

C. Escribe cuatro oraciones. Usa una palabra del vocabulario en cada oración.

_____

_____

_____

_____

Name _____   Date _____

Value in Lines

Vocabulary Words

value   hatching   cross-hatching

A. The word value can have many meanings. Match each
meaning of value with the correct sentence.

_____ **1.** worth in money

_____ **2.** importance; worth

_____ **3.** to prize; regard highly

_____ **4.** darkness or lightness

a. Do you value your
friends?

b. Use dark values in the
shadows.

c. The value of the car is
$3,000.

d. Playtime has great
value for kids.

B. Draw lines in the boxes to show a very light value. Then,
draw lines to show darker and darker values. Use
hatching in the first two boxes and **cross-hatching** in the
last two boxes to change value. Remember that lines
drawn closer together look darker.

Darker Values
———————————————————→

Nombre _____   Fecha _____

El valor en las líneas

Palabras de vocabulario

valor   plumear   rayar con líneas entrecruzadas

A. La palabra valor puede tener muchos significados.
Empareja cada significado de valor con la oración correcta.

_____ **1.** valoración en moneda   **a.** ¿Valoras a tus amigos?

_____ **2.** importancia; valoración   **b.** Usa valores oscuros en
                                               los sombreados.

_____ **3.** apreciar; alta estima   **c.** El valor del auto es
                                               $3,000.

_____ **4.** oscuridad o claridad   **d.** El tiempo de recreo
                                               tiene un gran valor
                                               para los niños.

B. Traza líneas en los cuadros para mostrar un valor muy claro.
Luego, traza líneas para mostrar valores cada vez más oscuros.
Usa el **plumeado** en los dos primeros cuadros y el **rayado
con líneas entrecruzadas** en los dos últimos cuadros.
Recuerda que las líneas trazadas con menos espacio entre
ellas parecen ser más oscuras.

Valores más oscuros →

Name _____   Date _____

Value

Vocabulary Words

highlight	perception
shadow	value

A. Write **yes** beside the sentence if the vocabulary word is used correctly. Write **no** if the word is not used correctly. Then cross out the part that is wrong, and rewrite the sentence correctly on another sheet of paper.

_____ **1.** The spotlight created highlights in the dancers' hair.

_____ **2.** By adding more colors, you change the value in a painting.

_____ **3.** Your perception of the model changes as she walks toward you and away from you.

_____ **4.** The shadows around the pieces of fruit in this painting make it look flat and two-dimensional.

B. Label each picture using a word from the box.

value	shadow	highlights	perception

1.

_____

2.

_____

3.

_____

4.

_____

Nombre _____   Fecha _____

Valor

Palabras de vocabulario

claros   percepción
sombras   valor

A. Escribe **sí** al lado de la oración si la palabra de vocabulario se usa correctamente. Escribe **no** si la palabra no se usa correctamente. Luego tacha la parte incorrecta. Escribe la oración correctamente en otra hoja de papel.

_____ **1.** El proyector creó claros en el cabello de los bailarines.

_____ **2.** Al agregar más colores, cambias el valor en una pintura.

_____ **3.** Tu percepción de la modelo cambia cuando camina hacia ti y cuando se aleja.

_____ **4.** Las sombras alrededor de las frutas de esta pintura la hacen que se vea plana y bidimensional.

B. Rotula cada dibujo usando una palabra de la caja.

valor	sombra	claros	percepción

1.

_____

2.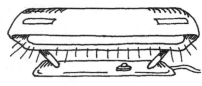

_____

3.

_____

4.

_____

Name _____   Date _____

Value Contrast

Vocabulary Words

contrast   cross-hatching   hatching
stippling   value

A. Beside each vocabulary word, draw an example or
illustration. Then, write a definition in your own words.

hatching [   ]   cross-hatching [   ]

_____   _____

_____   _____

_____   _____

stippling [   ]   contrast [   ]

_____   _____

_____   _____

_____   _____

B. Write a description of the
drawing. Use each of the
vocabulary words at
least once.

_____

_____

_____

_____

Nombre _____   Fecha _____

El contraste del valor

Palabras de vocabulario

contraste   rayar con líneas entrecruzadas   plumear
puntear   valor

A. Al lado de cada palabra de vocabulario, dibuja un ejemplo o
una ilustración. Luego, escribe una definición en tus propias
palabras.

plumear [   ]   rayar con líneas [   ]
                             entrecruzadas

_____   _____
_____   _____
_____   _____

puntear [   ]   contraste [   ]

_____   _____
_____   _____
_____   _____

B. Escribe una descripción del
dibujo. Usa cada una de las
palabras de vocabulario por
lo menos una vez.

_____
_____
_____
_____

Name _____   Date _____

Monochromatic Colors

Vocabulary Words

monochromatic	tint	hue	shade
primary hues		secondary hues	intermediate hues

A. Write a vocabulary word in the blank that means the same as the underlined words.

   1. The only <u>color</u> in the scene was blue. _____

   2. The top of the building was a blue <u>of a pale color</u>.

      _____

   3. On the right, the artist used a <u>darkened color</u> that was

      almost black. _____

   4. The painting of the lighthouse and the sea was <u>limited

      to a single color</u>. _____

B. Match each vocabulary word to its definition.

   ____ **1.** monochromatic   **a.** red, yellow, blue

   ____ **2.** hue   **b.** dark value

   ____ **3.** tint   **c.** light value

   ____ **4.** shade   **d.** orange, violet, green

   ____ **5.** primary hues   **e.** color

   ____ **6.** secondary hues   **f.** tints and shades of one color

   ____ **7.** intermediate   **g.** made by mixing primary and secondary hues
             hues

Nombre _____   Fecha _____

Colores monocromáticos

Palabras de vocabulario

monocromático	tinte	matiz	sombra
matiz primario	matiz secundario	matiz intermedio	

A. Escribe una palabra del vocabulario en el espacio en blanco que significa lo mismo que la palabra subrayada.

  1. El único <u>color</u> en la escena era azul. _____

  2. La parte superior del edificio era un azul <u>de un color pálido</u>. _____

  3. A la derecha, el artista usó un <u>color oscuro</u> que era casi negro. _____

  4. La pintura del faro y el mar estaba <u>limitada a un solo color</u>. _____

B. Empareja cada palabra del vocabulario con su definición.

  ____ **1.** monocromático   **a.** rojo, amarillo, azul

  ____ **2.** matiz   **b.** valor oscuro

  ____ **3.** tinte   **c.** valor claro

  ____ **4.** sombra   **d.** anaranjado, violeta, verde

  ____ **5.** matices primarios   **e.** color

  ____ **6.** matices secundarios **f.** tintes y sombras de un color

  ____ **7.** matices intermedios **g.** se crea al mezclar matices primarios y secundarios

Name _____   Date _____

Analogous Colors

Vocabulary Words

analogous colors   color scheme   nonobjective painting

A. Study the color wheel. Name two **analogous colors** for each color listed below.

1. blue   _____

        _____

2. red   _____

        _____

3. orange   _____

        _____

4. green   _____

        _____

5. blue-violet   _____

        _____

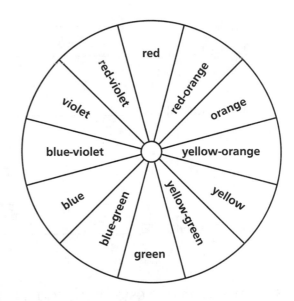

B. Imagine you are making a **nonobjective painting**. Choose a **color scheme**. Describe the colors, shapes, and lines used in your painting.

Your color scheme: _____

_____

_____

_____

_____

_____

Nombre _____   Fecha _____

Colores análogos

Palabras de vocabulario

colores análogos   esquema del color   pintura abstracta

A. Estudia el círculo cromático. Nombra los dos **colores análogos** para cada color enumerado a continuación.

1. azul   _____

   _____

2. rojo   _____

   _____

3. anaranjado   _____

   _____

4. verde   _____

   _____

5. azul violeta   _____

   _____

B. Imagínate que estás haciendo una **pintura abstracta**. Escoge un **esquema del color**. Describe los colores, las figuras y las líneas que usaste en tu dibujo.

Tu esquema del color: _____

_____

_____

_____

_____

_____

Name _____   Date _____

Complementary Colors

Vocabulary Words

complementary color   color intensity   adornment

A. Name the colors in the six pairs of
complementary colors shown on the
color wheel.

1. _____ _____

2. _____ _____

3. _____ _____

4. _____ _____

5. _____ _____

6. _____ _____

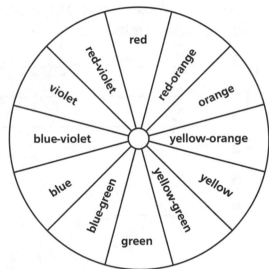

B. Room 10 in the new library is for group activities,
like meetings. Room 12 is for quiet reading and study.
How would you paint the rooms? Remember, bright hues
often make people feel active; less intense hues make them
feel calm.

1. What intensity of color would you use in Room 10?

low-intensity   high-intensity

2. What intensity of color would you use in Room 12?

low-intensity   high-intensity

C. Name three **adornments** for a person and a room.

1. Person   _____ _____ _____

2. Room   _____ _____ _____

Nombre _____   Fecha _____

Colores complementarios

Palabras de vocabulario

color complementario   intensidad de color   adorno

A. Nombra los colores en los seis pares de colores complementarios que se muestran en el círculo cromático.

1. _____   _____
2. _____   _____
3. _____   _____
4. _____   _____
5. _____   _____
6. _____   _____

B. El salón 10 de la biblioteca nueva es para actividades en grupo tales como reuniones. El salón 12 es para lectura y estudio. ¿Cómo pintarías los salones? Recuerda, los colores brillantes a menudo hacen que las personas se sientan enérgicas y los colores menos intensos las hacen sentir calmadas.

   1. ¿Qué intensidad de color usarías en el salón 10?

   baja intensidad   alta intensidad

   2. ¿Qué intensidad de color usarías en el salón 12?

   baja intensidad   alta intensidad

C. Nombra tres **adornos** para una persona y un salón.

   1. Persona   _____ _____ _____
   2. Salón   _____ _____ _____

Name _____   Date _____

Warm and Cool Colors

Vocabulary Words

warm color   cool color

A. Write cool or warm to tell what kind of color you might choose to show each mood or feeling in a painting. Then name two hues that are examples of the kind of color you chose.

	Warm or Cool?	**Colors You Might Use**	
1. happiness	_____	_____	_____
2. loneliness	_____	_____	_____
3. excitement	_____	_____	_____
4. anger	_____	_____	_____
5. sadness	_____	_____	_____

B. Use vocabulary words and color words to complete the puzzle.

1. warm color, often in flowers
2. sign of danger, fiery hue
3. mixture of two warm colors
4. green, blue, or violet
5. red, orange, or yellow
6. colors of grass and sky
7. color that mixes warm and cool

Nombre _____   Fecha _____

Colores cálidos y frescos

Palabras de vocabulario

color cálido   color fresco

A. Escribe fresco o cálido para indicar qué clase de color debes escoger para mostrar cada ánimo o sentimiento en un dibujo. Luego, nombra dos matices que sean ejemplos de la clase de color que escogiste.

	¿Cálido o fresco?	Colores que puedes usar
1. felicidad	_____	_____
2. soledad	_____	_____
3. emoción	_____	_____
4. enojo	_____	_____
5. tristeza	_____	_____

B. Usa las palabras del vocabulario y los colores para completar el acertijo.

1. colores de la grama y el cielo

2. mezcla de dos colores cálidos

3. signo de peligro, color ardiente

4. color que mezcla cálido y fresco

5. rojo, anaranjado o amarillo

6. color cálido, a menudo en las flores

7. verde, azul o violeta

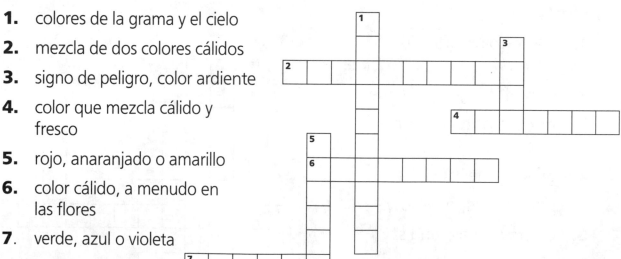

Name _____   Date _____

Visual Rhythm and Movement

Vocabulary Words

visual rhythm	alternate rhythm	regular rhythm
pattern	random rhythm	flowing rhythm
progressive rhythm	motif	

Complete the paragraph with vocabulary words.

Rhythm is all around us. There's rhythm in poetry, in music, and in a beautiful building. Rhythm we can see is called _____. For a design on a building, architects often choose objects that are connected in some way. This group of objects is called the

_____. It can be repeated over and over in a border around the building. This makes a(n)

_____. If the border is repeated with equal amounts of space between, the building shows

_____. If the architect uses more than one group of objects and repeats them one after the other, the building shows a(n) _____. If groups of objects are repeated in no special order, they create _____. Imagine a group of objects that is repeated many times. Then imagine that one thing in that group changes a little every time it is repeated. That is called _____. Some groups of objects are made up of wavy lines. These groups give the building a(n) _____.

Nombre _____   Fecha _____

Ritmo y movimiento visual

Palabras de vocabulario

ritmo visual	ritmo alterno	ritmo regular
patrón	ritmo aleatorio	ritmo continuo
ritmo progresivo	motivo	

Completa el párrafo con las palabras de vocabulario.

El ritmo nos rodea. Hay ritmo en la poesía, la música y en un bello edificio. El ritmo que podemos ver se llama

_____. Para un diseño de un edificio, los arquitectos a menudo escogen objetos que se conectan de alguna manera. A este grupo de objetos se le llama el

_____. Se puede repetir una y otra vez en un borde alrededor del edificio. Esto forma un

_____. Si el borde se repite con espacios iguales entre sí, el edificio muestra

_____. Si el arquitecto usa más de un grupo de objetos y los repite uno después del otro,

el edificio muestra un _____. Si grupos de objetos se repiten sin un orden en particular crean

_____. Imagínate un grupo de objetos que se repiten muchas veces. Luego, imagínate que una cosa en ese grupo cambia un poco cada vez que se repite. Esto se

conoce como _____. Algunos grupos de objetos están hechos de líneas curvas. Estos grupos le dan

al edificio un _____.

Name _____   Date _____

Color and Visual Rhythm

Vocabulary Words

color scheme	complementary colors
visual rhythm	monochromatic color scheme
cool color	analogous color scheme
warm color	

A. Use vocabulary words to complete these statements.

1. A color in a painting of a campfire is likely to be a(n)

   _____; a color in a painting of

   the night sky is likely to be a(n) _____.

2. An artist plans how he or she will organize colors in a

   design. This plan is the artist's _____.

3. An artist can't use either analogous or complementary

   colors if a(n) _____
   has been planned.

4. Red and blue are _____, so

   they can't be used in a(n) _____.

5. A pleasing pattern in a painting creates

   _____.

B. Answer the questions.

1. What is the difference between a monochromatic
   color scheme and an analogous color scheme?

   _____

2. What would be included in a monochromatic color
   scheme based on the color blue?

   _____

Nombre _____   Fecha _____

Color y ritmo visual

Palabras de vocabulario

esquema del color	colores complementarios
ritmo visual	esquema monocromático del color
color fresco	esquema análogo del color
color cálido	

A. Usa las palabras de vocabulario para completar estos enunciados.

1. Un color en una pintura de una hoguera es muy probable que

sea un _____; un color en una pintura del

cielo en la noche es probable que sea un

_____.

2. Un artista planifica cómo organizará los colores en un

diseño. Este plan es el _____ del artista.

3. Un artista no puede usar ni colores análogos ni complementarios

si se ha planificado un _____.

4. Rojo y azul son _____ así que no

se pueden usar en un _____.

5. Un patrón placentero en una pintura crea _____.

B. Contesta las preguntas.

1. ¿Cuál es la diferencia entre un esquema monocromático del
color y un esquema análogo del color?

_____

2. ¿Qué se incluiría en un esquema monocromático del color

basado en el color azul?_____

Copyright © SRA/McGraw-Hill. Permission is granted to reproduce this page for classroom use.

Name _____   **Date** _____

Positive and Negative Space

Vocabulary Words

space   negative space
positive space   shape reversal

A. For each form below, draw lines to the **positive spaces**
and **negative spaces** and label them.

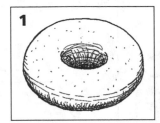   _____

   _____

B. Circle the figure that illustrates a **shape reversal**.

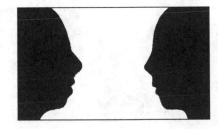   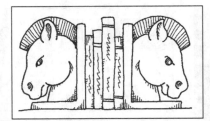   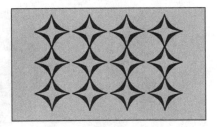

C. **Space** has many meanings. Match each sentence to the
correct definition.

____ **1.** region outside Earth's
atmosphere

____ **2.** the area inside a room

____ **3.** area surrounding or
within an object

____ **4.** to separate

a. There is plenty of space in this office.

b. Space your rows 18 inches apart.

c. The shuttle will blast off for space
tomorrow.

d. The artist created space around the boat
by placing a wave before and behind it.

Now, circle the definition of space that is used in art.

Nombre _____   Fecha _____

Espacio positivo y negativo

Palabras de vocabulario

espacio   espacio negativo
espacio positivo   figura inversa

A. Para cada forma a continuación, traza líneas a los **espacios positivos** y **negativos** y rotúlalos.

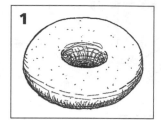
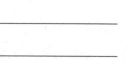

B. Encierra en un círculo la figura que ilustra una **figura inversa**.

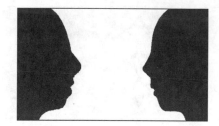
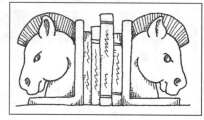
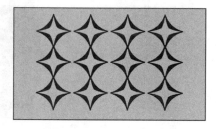

C. El **espacio** tiene muchos significados. Empareja cada oración con la definición correcta.

_____ **1.** región fuera de la atmósfera terrestre

_____ **2.** el área dentro de un salón

_____ **3.** área alrededor o dentro de un objeto

_____ **4.** separar

a. Hay suficiente espacio en esta oficina.

b. Coloca tus hileras con espacios de 18 pulgadas.

c. El transbordador despegará hacia el espacio mañana.

d. El artista creó un espacio alrededor del bote colocando una ola detrás y otra delante del mismo.

Ahora, encierra en un círculo la definición de espacio que se usa en arte.

Name _____   **Date** _____

Positive and Negative Space Reversal

Vocabulary Words

progressive reversal   progressive   tessellation

A. Write **true** if the statement is true. Write **false** if the statement is false.

_____   **1.** A sudden change is a progressive change.

_____   **2.** In art, progressive reversal describes a gradual reversal in positive and negative space.

_____   **3.** A tessellation is the same as a progressive reversal.

_____   **4.** Positive and negative spaces in a tessellation fit together like puzzle pieces.

_____   **5.** In a progressive reversal, an object may change in size, shape, or color.

B. Explain the meaning of each term.

Progressive reversal

_____

_____

_____

Tessellation

_____

_____

_____

Nombre _____   Fecha _____

Espacio positivo y negativo inversos

Palabras de vocabulario

inverso progresivo   progresivo   teselado

A. Si la declaración es verdadera, escribe **verdadero**. Si es falsa, escribe **falso**.

_____   **1.** Un cambio rápido es un cambio progresivo.

_____   **2.** En arte, el inverso progresivo describe un inverso gradual en el espacio positivo y negativo.

_____   **3.** Un teselado es lo mismo que un inverso progresivo.

_____   **4.** Los espacios positivo y negativo en un teselado encajan como las piezas de un rompecabezas.

_____   **5.** En un inverso progresivo, un objeto puede cambiar en tamaño, figura o color.

B. Explica el significado de cada término.

Inverso progresivo

_____

_____

_____

Teselado

_____

_____

_____

Name _____   Date _____

Texture

Vocabulary Words

texture   imitated texture   visual texture

A. Are the following textures **tactile** or **visual**? If you can
feel the texture, write **tactile**. If you can know the texture
only by what you see, write **visual**.

_____ **1.** a computer image of bark

_____ **2.** a woven leather belt

_____ **3.** a photograph of a peach

_____ **4.** a nubby, wool Navajo rug

_____ **5.** a drawing of a stone house

B. Name something that has each of the textures. Tell how
you could create a visual texture that looks rough or
smooth.

1. rough _____

_____

_____

2. smooth _____

_____

_____

C. Write the vocabulary word that answers the riddle.

1. "I make you think that I feel like a familiar object. You
believe you can reach out and touch me. But when
you try, you feel only paint or paper." I am

_____.

Nombre _____   Fecha _____

Textura

Palabras de vocabulario

textura   textura imitada   textura visual

A. ¿Son las siguientes texturas **táctiles** o **visuales**? Si puedes palpar la textura escribe **táctil**. Si puedes reconocer la textura sólo con verla escribe **visual**.

_____ **1.** una imagen de computadora de un ladrido

_____ **2.** un cinturón de cuero tejido

_____ **3.** una fotografía de un durazno

_____ **4.** una alfombra navajo con nudos de algodón

_____ **5.** un dibujo de una casa de piedra

B. Nombra algo que tenga cada una de las siguientes texturas. Indica cómo puedes crear una textura visual que parezca áspera o suave.

1. áspera _____

_____

_____

2. suave _____

_____

_____

C. Escribe la palabra de vocabulario que contesta el acertijo.

1. "Te hago pensar que tengo la textura de un objeto conocido. Tú crees que me puedes alcanzar y tocar. Pero cuando lo intentas, sólo tocas pintura o papel". Soy una

_____.

Name _____   Date _____

Architectural Form and Texture

Vocabulary Word

form

A. Imagine you can remove the depth from these three-dimensional forms. Draw a picture of a two-dimensional shape that is similar to each form.

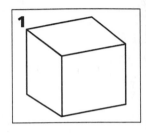 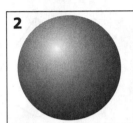 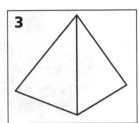 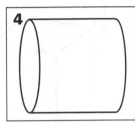

B. Describe two shading techniques that can be used to change a shape into a **form**.

1. _____

_____

2. _____

_____

Nombre _____   Fecha _____

Forma y textura arquitectónicas

Palabra de vocabulario

forma

A. Imagínate que puedes quitarle la profundidad a estas formas tridimensionales. Haz un dibujo de una figura bidimensional que sea parecida a cada forma.

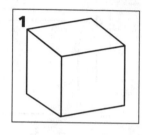
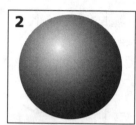
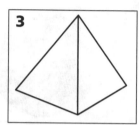
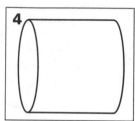

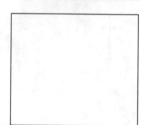

B. Describe dos técnicas de sombreado que se pueden usar para cambiar una figura a una **forma**.

1. _____

   _____

2. _____

   _____

Name _____   Date _____

Architectural Shape and Visual Texture

Vocabulary Words

architecture   architect

A. Read the word history for **architect** and answer the question.

> **Architect** comes from the Greek words **archi-**, meaning "chief" or "master," and **tekton**, meaning "carpenter" or "builder."

In what way is the architect for a building or a bridge the "master builder"? _____

_____

B. Complete the sentences with a vocabulary term.

1. A person who designs buildings is called an

_____.

2. The Empire State Building and the Sears Tower are examples of two different styles of

_____.

C. **Architecture** is both an art and a science. Underline phrases in the following paragraph that describe it as an art.

Architecture is the art and science of designing buildings. This is done to make them beautiful in form and proportion as well as suited to their use. Architecture uses the most advanced methods to create structures that are as strong, safe, and comfortable as possible. It also seeks to create structures that are based on certain ideas of proportion, scale, and beauty.

CONEXIONES CON EL ARTE
GRADO 5   Unidad 3, Lección 5

Nombre _____   **Fecha** _____

Figura arquitectónica y textura visual

Palabras de vocabulario

arquitectura   arquitecto

A. Lee la historia de la palabra **arquitecto** y contesta la pregunta.

Arquitecto se origina de las palabras griegas **arkhos**, que significa "jefe" o "maestro", y **tektôn**, que significa "carpintero" u "obrero".

¿De qué manera el arquitecto es el "maestro de obras" para un edificio o un puente? _____

_____

B. Completa las oraciones con un término del vocabulario.

1. Una persona que diseña edificios se llama

_____.

2. El edificio del Empire State y la torre Sears son ejemplos

de dos estilos diferentes de _____.

C. La **arquitectura** es tanto un arte como una ciencia. Subraya las frases que la describen como un arte en el siguiente párrafo.

La arquitectura es el arte y la ciencia de diseñar edificios. Esto se hace para que sean bellos en forma y proporción así como también para su uso práctico. La arquitectura usa los métodos más avanzados para crear estructuras que sean tan fuertes, seguras y cómodas como sea posible. También se trata de crear estructuras que estén basadas en ciertas ideas de proporción, escala y belleza.

Name _____   Date _____

Form and Tactile Texture

Vocabulary Words

form   shiny
tactile texture   matte
rough   armature
smooth

Complete the puzzle using the vocabulary words.

1. Has length, width, and depth.
2. With the _____ finish, your photos don't shine much.
3. You can feel a _____ texture.
4. The _____ texture makes the picture surface uniformly light.
5. A sculptor needs an _____.
6. Sandpaper has a _____ texture.
7. Glossy prints have a _____ finish.

Nombre _____   Fecha _____

Forma y textura táctil

Palabras de vocabulario

forma	brillante
textura táctil	mate
áspera	armadura
suave	

Completa el acertijo usando las palabras de vocabulario.

1. Tiene alto, ancho y profundidad.

2. Con el acabado _____, tus fotos no brillarán tanto.

3. Los grabados lustrosos tienen un acabado _____.

4. Un papel lija tiene una textura _____.

5. Un escultor necesita una _____.

6. La textura _____ hace que la superficie de la pintura tenga claridad uniforme.

7. Puedes palpar una textura _____.

Name _____   Date _____

Proportion

Vocabulary Words

proportion   body proportion

A. You can analyze how a word is built to understand its meaning. Answer the following questions about the word **proportion**.

   1. If you take the prefix **pro-** away from *proportion*, what word do you have? _____

   2. What does this smaller word mean?

   _____

   3. **Proportion** in art is concerned with size relationships between parts. Write a sentence that includes **body proportion**. Make sure your sentence is about proportion in art. _____

   _____

   _____

B. **Proportion** has several meanings. Circle the two sentences where proportion relates to art.

   A large proportion of students bring lunch to school.

   The dog's tiny eyes and huge nose seemed out of proportion.

   The small hands were in proportion to the child's body.

   Only a small proportion of flowers bloomed this spring.

Nombre _____   Fecha _____

Proporción

Palabras de vocabulario

proporción   proporción corporal

A. Puedes analizar cómo está construida una palabra para entender su significado. Contesta las siguientes preguntas acerca de la palabra **proporción**.

1. Si le quitas el prefijo **pro** a *proporción*, ¿qué palabra te queda? _____

2. ¿Qué significa esta palabra más pequeña? _____
_____

3. La **proporción** en arte trata del tamaño entre las partes. Escribe una oración que incluya **proporción corporal**. Asegúrate de que tu oración trate sobre la proporción en el arte.

_____

_____

B. La **proporción** tiene diferentes significados. Encierra en un círculo las dos oraciones donde la proporción está relacionada con arte.

Una gran proporción de estudiantes lleva el almuerzo a la escuela.

Los diminutos ojos del perro y la enorme nariz parecen estar fuera de proporción.

Las manitos parecían estar en proporción con el cuerpo del niño.

Sólo una pequeña proporción de flores florecieron esta primavera.

Name _____   Date _____

Scale

Vocabulary Words

scale   realistic scale   unrealistic scale

A. The idea of scale builds on the idea of proportion. Scale allows you to check proportions by measuring a model against what it represents. Fill in each blank with the word **scale** or **proportion**.

When you draw objects, you try to give them the same

_____ as they have in life. That is, you try to

give their parts the same relative sizes. _____

helps you to do this through measurement. The same principle is used in mapmaking. On a map, for example, a

_____ may make one inch equal to one mile. Similarly, on a ruler, the marks spaced out for measuring

objects are a kind of _____.

B. If the size relationship is about right, write **realistic scale**. If it is not reasonable, write **unrealistic scale**.

1. _____   2. _____   3. _____

C. Think of two objects. On the back of this page, draw two pictures of the objects, one with the objects in realistic scale and one with the objects in unrealistic scale.

Nombre _____   Fecha _____

Escala

Palabras de vocabulario

escala   escala real   escala irreal

A. La idea de escala se basa en la idea de proporción. La escala te permite comprobar proporciones midiendo un modelo contra lo que representa. Llena los espacios en blanco con la palabra **escala** o **proporción**.

Cuando dibujas objetos, tratas de darle la misma

_____ que tienen en la vida real. Es decir, tratas de darles a sus partes los mismos tamaños relativos. La

_____ te ayuda a realizar esto a través de la medida. El mismo principio se usa en cartografía. Por ejemplo,

en un mapa, una _____ puede hacer que una pulgada sea igual a una milla. De forma similar, en una regla las marcas espaciadas para medir los objetos son un tipo

de _____.

B. Si la relación de tamaño es casi correcta, escribe **escala real**. Si no es razonable, escribe **escala irreal**.

1. _____   2. _____   3. _____

C. Piensa en dos objetos. Detrás de esta página, haz dos dibujos de los objetos, uno con los objetos en escala real y otro con los objetos en escala irreal.

Name _____   **Date** _____

Facial Proportions

Vocabulary Words

facial proportions   profile proportions   central axis

A. Complete each sentence with the correct vocabulary word.

1. Use _____ _____ to draw eyes, ears, mouth, nose, and hair in the correct places on a face.

2. These lines include three horizontal lines dividing the head into fourths and a _____ _____, a vertical line that divides the head in half.

3. When the face is turned in side view, use _____ _____ to see that the features are proportional and correctly placed.

B. Study the examples of facial and profile proportions. Decide which term fits each descriptive phrase. Write **facial** or **profile** in the blank to show which type of proportion is involved.

_____   **1.** vertical line that divides face in half

_____   **2.** eyes appear on the middle horizontal line

_____   **3.** chin, eye, and ear form points of a triangle

_____   **4.** a side view

_____   **5.** space between eyes is one eye length

_____   **6.** a front view

Nombre _____   Fecha _____

Proporciones faciales

Palabras de vocabulario

proporciones faciales   proporciones de perfil   eje central

A. Completa cada oración con la palabra de vocabulario correcta.

1. Usa _____ para dibujar los ojos, las orejas, la boca, la nariz y el cabello en los lugares de la cara que corresponde.

2. Estas líneas incluyen tres líneas horizontales que dividen la cabeza en cuartos y un _____, una línea vertical que divide la cabeza en dos.

3. Cuando la cara se voltea de lado, usa _____ para observar que los rasgos están en proporción y están colocados correctamente.

B. Estudia los ejemplos de proporciones facial y de perfil. Decide qué término corresponde con cada frase descriptiva. Escribe **facial** o **de perfil** en el espacio en blanco para mostrar qué tipo de proporción se describe.

_____   **1.** la línea vertical que divide la cara en dos

_____   **2.** los ojos aparecen en el medio de la línea horizontal

_____   **3.** la barbilla, el ojo y la oreja forman puntos de un triángulo

_____   **4.** una vista lateral

_____   **5.** el espacio entre los ojos es una distancia ocular

_____   **6.** una vista frontal

Name _____   Date _____

Exaggeration

Vocabulary Word

exaggeration

A. Use the history of the word **exaggerate** and the definition given below to answer the questions.

Exaggerate comes from the Latin verb **exaggerare**, which means "to heap up" or "to increase."

   1. How is the meaning of **exaggerare** like the meaning

   of **exaggerate**? _____

   2. If a political cartoon exaggerates a woman's nose,

   what does it do? _____

   3. If you exaggerate your piano-playing ability, what do

   you say? _____

B. Put a ✓ beside each statement that contains an exaggeration.

   _____ **1.** His feet were as big as boats.

   _____ **2.** The butterfly drifted slowly and aimlessly.

   _____ **3.** I'm so excited about our trip.

   _____ **4.** They cheered so loudly, they raised the roof.

   _____ **5.** I've told you a million times not to exaggerate.

C. In the space to the right, draw a face in which the eyes are exaggerated.

Nombre _____   Fecha _____

Exageración

Palabra de vocabulario

exagerar

A. Usa la historia de la palabra **exagerar** y la definición a
continuación para contestar las preguntas.

Exagerar se origina del verbo latín **exaggerare** que significa
"amontonar" o "aumentar".

1. ¿En qué se parece el significado de **exaggerare** al

    significado de **exagerar**? _____

2. Si una caricatura política exagera la nariz de una mujer,

    ¿qué se logra?_____

3. Si exageraras tu habilidad de tocar piano, ¿qué dirías?

    _____

B. Coloca una marca de cotejo (✓) al lado de cada enunciado
que contenga una exageración.

_____ **1.** Sus pies eran tan grandes como botes.

_____ **2.** La mariposa voló despacio y a la deriva.

_____ **3.** Estoy tan emocionado acerca de nuestro viaje.

_____ **4.** Ellos vitorearon tan alto que levantaron el techo.

_____ **5.** Te he dicho millones de veces que no exageres.

C. En el espacio a continuación,
dibuja una cara exagerando
los ojos.

Name _____   **Date** _____

Distortion

Vocabulary Word

distortion

A. Complete the statements below to show how **distortion** and **exaggeration** are the same and how they are different.

Exaggeration and distortion are alike because they both

_____. However, when you exaggerate

something, you merely _____ it. When

you distort something, you may _____.
Here are several ways to distort an object in art:

(1) _____

(2) _____

(3) _____

B. Look at the drawing. In the boxes, redraw the clock face, distorting it as the labels indicate.

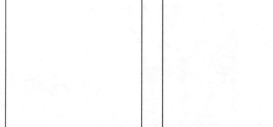

1. twist   **2.** squash   **3.** stretch

Nombre _____   Fecha _____

Distorsión

Palabra de vocabulario

distorsión

A. Completa los siguientes enunciados para mostrar en qué
se parecen y en qué se diferencian la **distorsión** y la
exageración.

La exageración y la distorsión se parecen porque las dos

_____. Sin embargo, cuando exageras

algo tan sólo lo _____. Cuando

distorsionas algo, quizás lo _____. Éstas

son varias maneras de distorsionar un objeto en arte:

(**1**) _____

(**2**) _____

(**3**) _____

B. Observa el dibujo. En los cuadros, dibuja
nuevamente la esfera del reloj y
distorsiónala como los rótulos lo indican.

```
[                ] [                ] [                ]
[                ] [                ] [                ]
[                ] [                ] [                ]
[                ] [                ] [                ]
```

1. torcer   **2.** aplastar   **3.** estirar

Name _____   **Date** _____

Scale and Proportion

Vocabulary Words

body proportions   ratio   scale

A. Write the vocabulary word that fits the details.

- Compares two things
- A proportion expressed as numbers

_____

- Head compared to body
- Size of one part related to size of another part

_____

- Uses a standard reference
- Measures according to a fixed, agreed upon proportion

_____

B. Read the paragraph. Then, answer the questions.

In ancient Greece, artists used a ratio called the **Golden Mean** to create pleasing body proportions. The Golden Mean said that from head to navel should be a length of 1 unit and from navel to toes should be a length of 1.6 units. Then the form would have the best arrangement and proportions.

1. What is the Golden Mean? _____

2. What is the proper ratio for head to navel and navel to toes, according to this rule? _____

3. Which of the following body proportions follow the Golden Mean? Circle the letters.

    a. 2 feet: 3.2 feet

    b. 1.5 feet: 3 feet

    c. 3 feet: 4.8 feet

Nombre _____   Fecha _____

Escala y proporción

Palabras de vocabulario

proporciones corporales   razón   escala

A. Escribe la palabra de vocabulario que corresponda con la descripción.

- Compara dos cosas
- Una proporción expresada como números

_____

- La cabeza comparada con el cuerpo
- El tamaño de una parte en relación con el tamaño de otra

_____

- Usa una referencia promedio
- Las medidas de acuerdo con una proporción fija y establecida

_____

B. Lee el párrafo. Luego, contesta las preguntas.

En la antigua Grecia, los artistas usaban una razón llamada el **justo medio** para crear proporciones corporales placenteras. El justo medio indica que desde la cabeza hasta el ombligo debía haber una distancia de 1 unidad y desde el ombligo hasta los dedos del pie debía haber una distancia de 1.6 unidades. Así, la forma tendría la mejor disposición y proporción.

1. ¿Qué es el justo medio? _____

2. ¿Cuál es la razón adecuada desde la cabeza hasta el ombligo y desde el ombligo hasta los dedos de los pies de

acuerdo con esta regla?_____

3. ¿Cuál de las siguientes proporciones corporales sigue las reglas del justo medio? Encierra en un círculo las letras.

    a. 2 pies: 3.2 pies   **b.** 1.5 pies: 3 pies

    c. 3 pies: 4.8 pies

Name _____   Date _____

Formal Balance

Vocabulary Words

balance	symmetry	formal balance
relief print	central axis	

A. Three of the vocabulary words have a special relationship. Fill in the blanks to show how they are related.

1. _____ means "harmonious arrangement."

2. _____ is "a kind of harmonious arrangement, with equal elements."

3. _____ is "an arrangement with halves that are mirror images of each other."

B. Use vocabulary words to complete the puzzle.

1. Having similar elements on the right and the left sides

2. Arrangement with two exactly balanced halves

3. Harmonious arrangement

4. Image printed from a raised surface

5. Line along which something is evenly divided

Nombre _____   Fecha _____

Equilibrio formal

Palabras de vocabulario

equilibrio	simetría	equilibrio formal
grabado en relieve	eje central	

A. Tres de las palabras de vocabulario tienen una relación especial.
Completa los espacios en blanco para mostrar cómo se relacionan.

    1. _____ significa "arreglo armonioso".

    2. _____ es "un tipo de arreglo armonioso,
con elementos iguales".

    3. _____ es "un arreglo cuyas mitades son
imágenes idénticas".

B. Usa las palabras de
vocabulario para
completar el crucigrama.

    1. Tener elementos
semejantes en los
lados derecho e
izquierdo

    2. Arreglo con dos
mitades exactamente
equilibradas

    3. Arreglo armonioso

    4. Línea a través de la
cual algo se divide
equitativamente

    5. Imagen impresa de
una superficie que
sobresale.

Name _____   Date _____

Informal Balance

Vocabulary Words

informal balance   asymmetry   negative space

A. When you add prefixes **a-** or **in-** before a word, you add
the meaning "not" to the word. Explain how the following
pairs of terms are related in meaning.

   1. symmetry and asymmetry: _____

   _____

   _____

   2. formal balance and informal balance: _____

   _____

   _____

B. Explain how the use of negative space helps to balance
the two halves of this image.

_____

_____

_____

_____

Nombre _____   Fecha _____

Equilibrio informal

Palabras de vocabulario

equilibrio informal   asimetría   espacio negativo

A. Cuando agregas los prefijos **a** o **in** antes de una palabra,
agregas el significado de "no" a la palabra. Explica cómo el
significado de los siguientes pares de términos se relacionan.

1. simetría y asimetría _____

_____

_____

2. equilibrio formal y equilibrio informal _____

_____

_____

B. Explica cómo el uso del espacio negativo ayuda a equilibrar las
dos mitades de esta imagen.

_____

_____

_____

_____

Name _____   Date _____

Radial Balance

Vocabulary Words

radial balance   mandala

A. In each group, cross out any word or phrase that does not belong. Look up any word you are unsure of.

   1. Words that are related in meaning to **radial**: radiate, radius, radar, radiant

   2. Examples of **radial balance**: a sunflower, a human face, a mandala, a maple leaf, a bicycle wheel and spokes

   3. Elements you could label in a **mandala**: center point, central axis, wedges or sections of the circle, circular designs

B. Complete the sentences to show you understand the difference between radial and formal balance.

   In radial balance, lines or shapes radiate out from a

   _____. They are always spaced evenly at

   intervals around a _____. On the other

   hand, formal balance creates equal _____,
   which can be divided by a line down the center called the

   _____. The two halves on each side of

   this line are _____ of each other.

C. Circle each image that illustrates radial balance.

  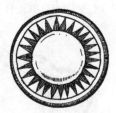 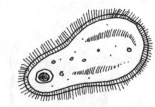

Nombre _____   Fecha _____

Equilibrio radial

Palabras de vocabulario

equilibrio radial   mandala

A. En cada grupo, tacha cualquier palabra o frase que no corresponda. Investiga cualquier palabra de la que no estés seguro.

 1. Palabras cuyo significado se relacionan con **radial**: radiar, radio, radar, radiante

 2. Ejemplos de **equilibrio radial**: un girasol, un rostro humano, un mandala, una hoja de arce, una llanta de bicicleta y un radio de una rueda

 3. Elementos de una pintura que podrías rotular en un **mandala**: punto central, eje central, cuñas o secciones del círculo, diseños circulares

B. Completa las oraciones para mostrar que comprendes la diferencia entre equilibrio radial y formal.

 En el equilibrio radial, las líneas o las figuras radian a partir de un

 _____. Siempre están colocadas a intervalos

 iguales alrededor de un _____. Por otra parte, el

 equilibrio formal crea _____ iguales, que se
 pueden dividir por medio de una línea atravesando el centro

 llamada _____. Las dos mitades a cada lado de

 esta línea son _____.

C. Encierra en un círculo cada imagen que ilustre el equilibrio radial.

   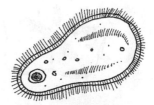

Name _____   Date _____

Perspective Techniques

Vocabulary Words

perspective   depth

A. Write the definition number beside the sentence that uses **perspective** with this meaning.

_____ **1.** The perspective from the hot-air balloon made the people and livestock below seem like ants.

_____ **2.** In a few years, you will be able to put this all in perspective.

_____ **3.** Using perspective, the artist makes the road appear to grow narrower until it disappears at the horizon.

a. ability to see things in a true relationship

b. art of drawing objects on a flat surface so that they appear to have depth and distance

c. the effect of distance on appearance of objects

B. What makes these images appear to have **depth**? Explain the perspective technique used to create each image.

1.

2.

_____   _____

_____   _____

_____   _____

_____   _____

_____   _____

Nombre _____   Fecha _____

Técnicas de perspectiva

Palabras de vocabulario

perspectiva   profundidad

A. Escribe el número de la definición al lado de la oración que use
este significado de **perspectiva**.

_____ **1.** La perspectiva desde un globo
aerostático hacía que las personas y el
ganado se vieran como hormigas.

_____ **2.** En unos cuantos años, podrás poner
todo esto en perspectiva.

_____ **3.** Con el uso de la perspectiva, el artista
logra que el camino parezca hacerse
más angosto hasta que desaparece
en el horizonte.

a. la habilidad de ver las cosas en
una relación verdadera

b. el arte de dibujar objetos en
una superficie plana de tal
forma que pareciera que
tuviera profundidad y distancia

c. el efecto de la distancia en la
apariencia de los objetos

B. ¿Qué hace que estas imágenes parezcan tener **profundidad**?
Explica la técnica de perspectiva usada para crear cada imagen.

1.

2.

_____   _____

_____   _____

_____   _____

_____   _____

Name _____   Date _____

Linear Perspective

Vocabulary Words

perspective   horizon line
linear perspective   vanishing point

A. Complete each analogy using a vocabulary word.

   1. *Close-up* is to *invisible* as *nearest object* is to

   _____.

   2. *Two dimensions* is to *three dimensions* as *flat image* is

   to _____.

B. Use a vocabulary word to complete each sentence.

   1. The area where Earth meets the sky is the

   _____.

   2. When you create the illusion of space in your painting,

   you have used a _____
   technique.

   3. A technique in which lines are used to show depth is

   _____.

C. Label the **vanishing point** and the **horizon line** on the
drawing. Draw a line from the word to the correct place in
the picture.

   _____   _____

Nombre _____   Fecha _____

Perspectiva lineal

Palabras de vocabulario

perspectiva   línea del horizonte
perspectiva lineal   punto de fuga

A. Completa cada analogía usando una palabra de vocabulario.

1. Una *toma de primer plano* es a *invisible* como el
    objeto más cercano es a _____.

2. *Dos dimensiones* son a *tres dimensiones* como
    una *imagen plana* es a _____.

B. Usa una palabra de vocabulario para completar cada oración.

1. El área donde la tierra y el cielo se encuentran es la
    _____.

2. Cuando creas la apariencia de espacio en una pintura,
    usas una técnica de _____.

3. La técnica en la cual se usan las líneas para mostrar
    profundidad es la _____.

C. Señala el **punto de fuga** y la **línea del horizonte** en el
    dibujo. Traza una línea desde la palabra hasta el lugar correcto
    en el dibujo.

_____   _____

Name _____   Date _____

Point of View and Direct Observation

Vocabulary Words

point of view   direct observation

A. Describe how a bicycle looks from four points of view.

_____

B. How does **direct observation** help an artist?

_____

C. Each person has described the same object from a different **point of view**. On each blank line, write the point of view (frontal, overhead, side, or back). Then, name the object described.

1. "It was coming at me fast. The rectangular glass was like a blank, staring eye and the wide strip of chrome bumper gleamed like teeth." _____

2. "It glided smoothly below me, magically, a shiny, rounded rectangle around a smaller square roaring along a concrete path." _____

3. "As it sped off, the rear lights blinked like the eyes of a monster. It seemed like a low creature rolling backwards into the darkness." _____

4. "As it rolled by, I had the impression of a dolphin, a sleek, streamlined shape with a long, elegant nose and tail. Of course, dolphins don't have round rubber fins!" _____

What is the name of the object? _____

Nombre _____   Fecha _____

Punto de vista y observación directa

Palabras de vocabulario

punto de vista   observación directa

A. Describe cómo se ve una bicicleta desde cuatro puntos de vista.

_____

B. ¿Cómo ayuda la **observación directa** al artista?

_____

C. Cada persona describió el mismo objeto desde un **punto de vista** diferente. En cada línea, escribe el punto de vista (frontal, aéreo, lateral o posterior) usado. Luego nombra el objeto descrito.

1. "Se aproximaba rápidamente. El vidrio rectangular era como un ojo en blanco mirándome fíjamente y el parachoques de franja ancha de cromo brillaba como dientes."

_____

2. "Se deslizaba suavemente debajo de mí, mágicamente, un rectángulo redondeado y brillante alrededor de un cuadrado más pequeño pasaba estruendosamente a lo largo del

camino." _____

3. "A medida que aceleraba, las luces posteriores titilaban como los ojos de un monstruo. Parecía una criatura pequeña

retrocediendo en la oscuridad." _____

4. "Al deslizarse a mi lado, me dio la impresión de que era un delfín, una figura lisa y aerodinámica con una nariz larga y elegante y una cola. Por supuesto, los delfines no tienen

escamas redondeadas de goma." _____

¿Cómo se llama el objeto? _____

Name _____   Date _____

Emphasis Through Contrast

Vocabulary Words

appliqué   isolation   emphasis
location   contrast

A. Use vocabulary words to complete the paragraph.

In a work of art, the artist may want to call attention to an area or part. He or she will design the artwork to give

_____ to that portion. This may be done in several ways: (1) The artist may stress the object through

_____, by placing it at the center; (2) he or she may draw attention to it through _____, by creating the element with a color, shape, or texture that differs sharply from the rest; or (3) the artist may give

emphasis through _____, which separates the object from the rest of the artwork by negative space.

B. On the lines below, explain what materials you would need to create an **appliqué** project.

_____

_____

C. Use a vocabulary word to complete each analogy.

   1. *Ignore* is to *overlook* as *accent* is to _____.

   2. *Help* is to *oppose* as *union* is to _____.

   3. *Differ* is to *difference* as *apply* is to _____.

   4. *Show* is to *tell* as *compare* is to _____.

Nombre _____   Fecha _____

Destacar a través del contraste

Palabras de vocabulario

aplicación	aislamiento	destaque
ubicación	contraste	

A. Usa las palabras de vocabulario para completar el párrafo.

En una obra de arte, es posible que el artista quiera recalcar
un área o una sección. Él o ella diseñará la obra de tal forma

que dicha porción se _____. Esto se puede
hacer de varias maneras: (1) El artista puede enfatizar el

objeto por medio de la _____ colocándolo en el
centro; (2) él o ella puede atraer la atención hacia ese punto

por medio del _____ creando el elemento con un
color, una figura o una textura muy diferente del resto; o (3) el

artista puede recalcarlo por medio del _____ lo cual
separa el objeto del resto de la obra a través del espacio negativo.

B. En las siguientes líneas, explica qué materiales necesitarías
para crear un proyecto de una **aplicación**.

_____

C. Usa una palabra de vocabulario para completar cada analogía.

1. *Ignorar* es a *pasar por alto* como *acento* es a

_____

2. *Ayudar* es a *oponer* como *unión* es a _____

3. *Diferir* es a *diferencia* como *aplicar* es a _____

4. *Mostrar* es a *decir* como *comparar* es a _____

Name _____   Date _____

Emphasis as a Focal Point

Vocabulary Words

emphasis   warp threads
focal point   weft threads

A. How is **focal point** like **focus**? Think about the meaning
of focal point. Study the example sentences using **focus**.
Then, write your explanation.

Do you like to be the **focus** of attention?

Focus on the problem and you will think of a solution.

_____

_____

B. Label the **warp** and **weft** threads on the loom. Then,
write **warp** or **weft** on the blank beside each statement.

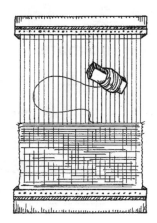

_____   **1.** These threads must be put on the loom first.

_____   **2.** These threads run vertically.

_____   **3.** These threads run horizontally.

_____   **4.** These threads hold the weaving in place.

_____   **5.** These threads are woven in one by one to
complete the weaving.

C. **Emphasis** and **focal point** are closely related in meaning.
Fill in the blanks to complete the following explanation of
their relationship.

In most artworks, the artist has in mind certain areas he
or she wants you to look at first or to look at longest.

_____ is the design technique the artist uses
to draw your eye to this area. The area itself on which

you focus is the _____.

Nombre _____   Fecha _____

El punto destacado como punto focal

Palabras de vocabulario

destacar   hilos de urdimbre   punto focal   hilos de trama

A. ¿En qué se parece el **punto focal** al **foco**? Piensa en el significado del punto focal. Estudia los ejemplos de oraciones en las que se usa el término **foco**. Luego escribe tu explicación.

¿Te gusta ser el **foco** de atención?

Si piensas en el **foco** del problema, puedes obtener la solución.

_____

_____

B. Señala los hilos de **urdimbre** y de **trama** en el telar. Luego, escribe **urdimbre** o **trama** en el espacio en blanco al lado de cada oración.

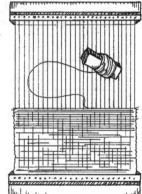

_____ **1.** Estos hilos deben ponerse primero en el telar.

_____ **2.** Estos hilos se extienden en dirección vertical.

_____ **3.** Estos hilos se extienden en dirección horizontal.

_____ **4.** Estos hilos sostienen el tejido en su lugar.

_____ **5.** Estos hilos se hilan uno por uno para completar el tejido.

C. Los significados de **destacar** y **punto focal** son parecidos. Llena los espacios en blanco para completar la siguiente explicación de su relación.

En la mayoría de las obras de arte, el artista tiene en mente ciertas áreas que quiere que el espectador vea primero o que vea por más tiempo. El _____ es la técnica de diseño que el artista usa para atraer la mirada del espectador a esta área. El área en sí en la que te fijas es el _____.

Name _____   Date _____

Variety

Vocabulary Words

variety   contrast

A. Use your understanding of the word **variety** to answer each question.

   1. What might a magazine titled *Variety* be like?

     _____

   2. If your wardrobe has variety, what is it like?

     _____

   3. What does the saying "Variety is the spice of life" mean?

     _____

B. Circle the words below that you think are related to **variety**. Use the context to figure out a meaning for each word you circle. Write the meaning on the blank lines.

   1. We have a varied menu. _____

   2. The varicolored petunias are striking. _____

   3. Eat various fruits and vegetables for good health.

     _____

C. In a cause-and-effect relationship, one thing or event (the cause) makes something else happen (the effect). Explain the cause-and-effect relationship between **variety** and **contrast**.

     _____

     _____

     _____

Nombre _____   Fecha _____

Variedad

Palabras de vocabulario

variedad   contraste

A. Usa lo que entiendas por la palabra **variedad** para contestar cada pregunta.

   1. ¿De qué trataría una revista llamada *Variedad*?

   _____

   2. Si hubiera variedad en tu vestuario, ¿cómo sería?

   _____

   3. ¿Qué quiere decir el dicho "la variedad es la sal de la vida"?

   _____

B. Encierra en un círculo las palabras a continuación que creas se relacionan con **variedad**. Usa el contexto para determinar un significado por cada palabra que encierres en un círculo. Escribe el significado en las líneas en blanco.

   1. Tenemos un menú variado. _____

   2. Las petunias multicolores son impresionantes.

   _____

   3. Come una serie de frutas y hortalizas para tener

   buena salud. _____

C. En una relación de causa y efecto, una cosa o un acontecimiento (la causa) hace que algo suceda (el efecto). Explica la relación de causa y efecto entre **variedad** y **contraste**.

_____

_____

_____

Name _____   Date _____

Harmony

Vocabulary Words

harmony   assemblage

A. Use the definitions for the vocabulary words to help you answer each question.

    1. How is an **assemblage** like a collage?

    _____

    2. How is an **assemblage** like a sculpture?

    _____

    3. **Harmony** comes from the Greek word **harmos**, meaning "a fitting." How do the parts of an artwork with harmony fit together?

    _____

    _____

    4. **Harmony** has various meanings. All of them have to do with combinations that are orderly, pleasing, and in agreement. Write a sentence comparing harmony in music with harmony in art.

    _____

    _____

B. Draw an example of lines in harmony. First, decide what mood or idea you want to convey. Then, create your design.

Nombre _____   Fecha _____

Armonía

Palabras de vocabulario

armonía   montaje

A. Usa las definiciones de las palabras de vocabulario para contestar cada pregunta.

   1. ¿En qué se parecen el **montaje** y el collaje?

   _____

   2. ¿En qué se parece un **montaje** a una escultura?

   _____

   3. **Armonía** proviene de la palabra griega **harmonia** que significa "arreglo". ¿Cómo forman un arreglo las diferentes partes de una obra de arte?

   _____

   _____

   4. El término **armonía** tiene varios significados. Todos tienen que ver con combinaciones ordenadas, agradables y concordantes. Escribe una oración en la que compares la armonía en la música y la armonía en el arte.

   _____

   _____

B. Dibuja un ejemplo de líneas en armonía. Primero, decide qué ambiente o idea quieres proyectar. Luego, crea tu diseño.

Name _____   Date _____

Environmental Unity

Vocabulary Words

unity   variety
harmony

A. Each group of words makes up a "family"—all created
   from a root with the same meaning. Find the word that
   does not belong in each family and cross it out. Then,
   beside each group, write the vocabulary word that
   belongs in the family.

   1. _____   united, untied, unified, union

   2. _____   variegated, variation, unvarying, varsity

   3. _____   harmless, harmonize, harmonica, harmonious

B. The sentences describe the flag below. In each blank, write the vocabulary word
   that fits.

   1. Contrasting stripes and stars and contrasting colors
      establish _____, or the use of different
      elements.

   2. There is _____ between the stars and
      stripes, too, for the stars represent today's fifty states,
      while the stripes represent the first colonies.

   3. Because each color and shape symbolizes something
      important about the United States, these different
      parts combine in powerful _____.

Nombre _____   Fecha _____

Unidad ambiental

Palabras de vocabulario

unidad   variedad   armonía

A. Cada grupo de palabras constituye una "familia"—todas creadas de una base con el mismo significado. Busca la palabra que no corresponde en cada familia y táchala. Luego, escribe la palabra de vocabulario que corresponde a la familia al lado de cada grupo.

1. _____   unido, uniforme, unir, unión

2. _____   variar, variación, invariable, universitario

3. _____   armazón, armonizar, armónica, armonioso

B. Las oraciones describen la bandera a continuación. En cada espacio en blanco, escribe la palabra de vocabulario correspondiente.

1. El contraste de las bandas y las estrellas y el contraste de

   los colores establecen la _____, o sea el uso de diferentes elementos.

2. También existe _____ entre las estrellas y las bandas ya que las estrellas representan los cincuenta estados actuales y las bandas representan las primeras colonias.

3. Ya que cada color y figura simboliza algo importante acerca de Estados Unidos, estas partes diferentes se

   combinan en una _____ poderosa.

Name _____   **Date** _____

Unity

Vocabulary Word

unity

Read the paragraph about **unity**. Then study the illustrations.
On the lines, explain why each thing that is pictured has unity.

> Unity is oneness or wholeness. It results from a
> combination of things that belong together. The pieces
> may be quite different, but when they are brought
> together in just the right way, they form a whole. The
> pieces themselves—or the work they do—have a common
> goal. The purpose or meaning of the finished piece comes
> from this exact combination of parts.

_____   _____

_____   _____

_____   _____

_____   _____

_____   _____

Nombre _____   **Fecha** _____

Unidad

Palabra de vocabulario

unidad

Lee el párrafo acerca de la **unidad**. Luego, estudia las ilustraciones. En las líneas, explica por qué cada cosa ilustrada tiene unidad.

> La unidad es integridad o totalidad. Es el resultado de una combinación de cosas entre las cuales existe una correspondencia. Las partes pueden ser muy diferentes, pero cuando se juntan de la manera correcta, forman un todo. Las partes en sí—o la función que cumplen—tienen un objetivo común. El propósito o significado de la obra final proviene de esta combinación exacta de las partes.

_____   _____

_____   _____

_____   _____

_____   _____

_____   _____

English
Answer Key

UNIT 1

Lesson 1

A.
1. zigzag
2. horizontal
3. diagonal
4. vertical
5. curved

B.
1. linear
2. vertically
3. horizon

C. zigzag; horizontal; vertical; curved

Lesson 2

1. free-form shape
2. shape
3. complex geometric shape
4. geometric shape

Geometric Shapes
  circle
  square
  triangle
  oval
  rectangle

Complex Geometric Shapes
  pentagon
  hexagon
  octagon
  parallelogram
  trapezoid

Lesson 3

A.
1. point of view
2. value
3. gradations
4. shading

B.
1. point of view
2. gradation
3. shading
4. value

C. Responses will vary.

Lesson 4

A.
1. c
2. d
3. a
4. b

B. Responses will vary but students should show the lightest value in the far left box and the darkest value in the far right box. The first two boxes should use a hatching technique, the last two, a cross-hatching technique.

Lesson 5

A. Rewritten sentences will vary but should include an explanation of the misused vocabulary word.
1. yes
2. No; students should write a new sentence explaining value as a function of lightness or darkness, not color or hue, i.e., by changing the lightness or darkness, you change the value in a painting.
3. yes
4. No; students should write a new sentence making it clear that shadows make objects in an artwork look three-dimensional, i.e., shadows...make it look round and three-dimensional.

B.
1. shadow
2. highlights
3. value
4. perception

Lesson 6

A. Definitions will vary but should include the following information:
hatching—shading using parallel lines
cross-hatching—shading using lines going in different or opposite directions
stippling—shading using dots or short marks
contrast—used by artists to show differences between two things when they are compared

B. Responses will vary.

UNIT 2

Lesson 1

A. 1. hue
2. tint
3. shade
4. monochromatic

B. 1. f
2. e
3. c
4. b
5. a
6. d
7. g

Lesson 2

A. 1. *Blue:* blue-green, blue-violet
2. *Red:* red-orange, red-violet
3. *Yellow:* yellow-orange, yellow-green
4. *Green:* yellow-green, blue-green
5. *Blue-violet:* blue, violet

B. Answers will vary but should address the color scheme, shapes, lines, and colors. Students should not mention a subject, since nonobjective paintings do not have a subject.

Lesson 3

A. 1.–6. Answers may appear in a differnt order, but pairs should be:
1. red, green
2. red-orange, blue-green
3. orange, blue
4. yellow-orange, blue-violet
5. yellow, violet
6. yellow-green, red-violet

B. 1. high-intensity
2. low-intensity

C. 1.–2. Answers will vary.

Lesson 4

A. Color choices will vary but should match choice of *warm* or *cool*.
1. warm
2. cool
3. warm
4. warm
5. cool

B. 1. yellow
2. red
3. orange
4. cool
5. warm
6. green and blue
7. violet

Lesson 5

A. visual rhythm; motif; pattern; regular rhythm; alternate rhythm; random rhythm; progressive rhythm; flowing rhythm

Lesson 6

A. 1. warm color; cool color
2. color scheme
3. monochromatic color scheme
4. complementary colors; analogous color scheme
5. visual rhythm

B. 1. A monochromatic color scheme includes values of only one color. An analogous color scheme includes several related colors—for example, yellow-green, green, and blue.
2. A monochromatic color scheme based on the color blue would include tints and shades of blue.

UNIT 3

Lesson 1

A. 1. Doughnut is positive space. Space around doughnut and in doughnut hole is negative space.
2. Tree is positive space. Space around tree is negative space.

B. Students should circle the first design with vase and faces.

C. 1. c
2. a
3. d
4. b
Students should circle the definition in item 3.

Lesson 2

A. 1. false
2. true
3. false
4. true
5. true

B. Answers may vary but could include the following:
Progressive reversal: when an object starts out as one object or form and slowly changes into another object or form.
Tessellation: a type of shape reversal that changes quickly and fits together like a puzzle.

Lesson 3

A. 1. visual
2. tactile
3. visual
4. tactile
5. visual

B. Answers will vary.

C. imitated texture or visual texture. (Imitated texture is a type of visual texture.)

Lesson 4

A. 1. Students should draw a square.
2. Students should draw a circle.
3. Students should draw a triangle.
4. Students should draw a circle or a rectangle.

B. Answers will vary but should describe two shading techniques, such as hatching, cross-hatching, stippling, or blending.

Lesson 5

A. The architect plans the bridge and oversees its construction.

B. 1. architect
2. architecture

C. art; beautiful in form and proportion; based on certain ideas of proportion, scale, and beauty

Lesson 6

1. form
2. matte
3. tactile
4. smooth
5. armature
6. rough
7. shiny

UNIT 4

Lesson 1

A. 1. portion
2. share or part
3. Sentences will vary but should focus on body proportion as a relationship in the size of the parts of the body.

B. Students should circle sentences 2 and 3.

Lesson 2

A. proportion; Scale; scale; scale

B. 1. realistic scale
2. unrealistic scale
3. realistic scale

C. Students should make two drawings of the same two objects, one showing them in realistic scale and one showing them in unrealistic scale.

Lesson 3

A. 1. facial proportions
2. central axis
3. profile proportions

B. 1. facial
2. facial
3. profile
4. profile
5. facial
6. facial

Lesson 4

A. 1. Both words describe an increase in size or amount.
2. It makes the nose bigger than it really is to call attention to it.
3. You say that you have greater ability than you really do.

B. Students should mark items 1, 4, and 5.

C. Students should draw a face with unusually large eyes.

Lesson 5

A. result in a change from the way something actually is; enlarge; change it in many different ways; (examples of distortion may vary)

B. 1.–3. Drawings will vary.

Lesson 6

A. ratio; body proportions; scale
B. 1. The ratio that expresses appropriate length of top and bottom of human form.
   2. 1:1.6, or 1 to 1.6
   3. a, c

UNIT 5

Lesson 1

A. 1. Balance
   2. Formal balance
   3. Symmetry
B. 1. formal balance
   2. symmetry
   3. balance
   4. relief print
   5. central axis

Lesson 2

A. Responses will vary but could include the following:
   1. Symmetry means that the parts of an object are mirror images of one another. Asymmetry means that the parts are not mirror images.
   2. In formal balance, like elements on each side have equal visual weight. In informal balance, there are *unlike* elements on each side, but they balance each other.
B. Responses will vary but should include the following: There is more negative space around the smaller triangles, which helps balance the larger positive space taken up by the large triangle.

Lesson 3

A. 1. radar
   2. a human face; a maple leaf
   3. central axis
B. center point; circle; halves; axis; mirror images
C. Students should circle the sand dollar and the china plate.

Lesson 4

A. 1. c
   2. a
   3. b

B. 1. Each tree is a little smaller than the one nearer the viewer. Since more distant objects appear smaller, we see the row of trees in the picture as stretching farther and farther away.
   2. The house covers part of the barn and silo, and this is how they would appear to us. Also, the house is lower and larger, making it seem closer to the viewer than the barn and silo.

Lesson 5

A. 1. vanishing point
   2. perspective
B. 1. horizon line
   2. perspective
   3. linear perspective
C. Students should label the horizon line and the vanishing point.

Lesson 6

A. Descriptions will vary but should mention the parts of a bicycle that would be obvious from the front (handlebars, front fender, front tire); from the side (handlebars, front and back wheels, fenders, frame, and seat); from overhead (handlebars, frame, seat, front and back fender); and from the back (seat, back fender, back tire).
B. Responses will vary but should include that the artist can learn more about the structure and details of an object through direct observation.
C. 1. frontal
   2. overhead
   3. back
   4. side
   The object is a car.

UNIT 6

Lesson 1

A. emphasis; location; contrast; isolation
B. Students should list several kinds and textures of fabric and glue, or needle and thread.
C. 1. emphasis
   2. isolation
   3. appliqué
   4. contrast

Lesson 2

A. Responses will vary but should indicate that both words relate to seeing and to what is central in an activity or object.

B.
1. warp
2. warp
3. weft
4. warp
5. weft

C. Emphasis; focal point

Lesson 3

A. Answers will vary but could include the following:
1. It might contain articles about a wide range of topics.
2. It contains many different types and styles of clothing.
3. If you do many things in life, you will not be bored.

B.
1. varied; containing many different things
2. varicolored; having several colors
3. various; different

C. Variety is used to create, or cause, contrast.

Lesson 4

A. 1–4. Answers will vary but may include:
1. Both involve attaching pieces of different materials to a surface.
2. Both are three-dimensional.
3. The parts fit together so that they seem to belong together.
4. Both place elements that are pleasing together; the elements in music are sounds and the elements in art are visual images.

B. Drawings will vary.

Lesson 5

A.
1. unity; cross out untied
2. variety; cross out varsity
3. harmony; cross out harmless

B.
1. variety
2. harmony
3. unity

Lesson 6

Responses will vary but could include the following:

Suspension Bridge: The cables, beams, pillars, and roadway are very different forms made from different materials, but they are combined gracefully. This beautiful and functional combination of materials and forms allows people to cross from one side of a river to the other.

ID Bracelet: The links, the nameplate, and the clasp are joined in a way that looks pleasing and that functions to hold the jewelry on the wearer's wrist. The different elements all have a rounded quality, like the rounded form of the wrist.

Spanish
Answer Key

UNIDAD 1

Lección 1

A. 1. en zigzag
2. horizontal
3. diagonal
4. vertical
5. curva
B. 1. lineal
2. verticalmente
3. horizonte
C. en zigzag; horizontal; verticales; curva

Lección 2

1. figura abstracta
2. figura
3. figura geométrica compleja
4. figura geométrica

Figuras geométricas
   círculo
   cuadrado
   triángulo
   óvalo
   rectángulo
Figuras geométricas complejas
   pentágono
   hexágono
   octágono
   paralelogramo
   trapecio

Lección 3

A. 1. punto de vista
2. valor
3. degradaciones
4. sombreado
B. 1. punto de vista
2. degradación
3. sombreado
4. valor
C. Las respuestas variarán.

Lección 4

A. 1. c
2. d
3. a
4. b
B. Las respuestas variarán, pero los estudiantes deben mostrar en el cuadro del extremo izquierdo el valor más claro y en el cuadro del extremo derecho el valor más oscuro. Los primeros dos cuadros deben usar una técnica de plumeado y los últimos dos una técnica de rayar con líneas entrecruzados.

Lección 5

A. Las oraciones variarán, pero deben incluir una explicación del uso incorrecto de la palabra de vocabulario.
1. sí
2. no. Los estudiantes deben escribir una nueva oración para explicar lo que es el valor con respecto a la claridad y la oscuridad, no con respecto al color. Por ejemplo: Al cambiar la claridad o la oscuridad, cambias el valor de una pintura.
3. sí
4. no. Los estudiantes deben escribir una nueva oración aclarando que las sombras hacen que un objeto en una obra artística se vean tridimensionales. Por ejemplo: Las sombras...lo hacen ver redondeado y tridimensional.
B. 1. sombra
2. claros
3. valor
4. percepción

Lección 6

A. Las definiciones variarán, pero deben incluir la siguiente información:
plumear—sombrear usando líneas paralelas
rayar con líneas entrecruzadas—sombrear usando líneas con direcciones diferentes u opuestas
puntear—sombrear usando puntos o marcas pequeñas
contraste—usado por los artistas para mostrar las diferencias entre dos cosas cuando se comparan
B. Las respuestas variarán.

UNIDAD 2

Lección 1

A. 1. color
2. tinte
3. sombra
4. monocromático

B. 1. f
2. e
3. c
4. b
5. a
6. d
7. g

Lección 2

A. 1. *Azul:* azul verdoso, azul violeta
2. *Rojo:* rojo anaranjado, rojo violeta
3. *Amarillo:* amarillo anaranjado, amarillo verdoso
4. *Verde:* amarillo verdoso, azul verdoso
5. *Azul violeta:* azul, violeta

B. Las respuestas variarán pero deben exponer el esquema del color, las figuras, las líneas y los colores. Los estudiantes no deben mencionar un tema ya que las pinturas abstractas no tienen un tema.

Lección 3

A. 1. rojo, verde
2. rojo anaranjado, azul verdoso
3. anaranjado, azul
4. amarillo anaranjado, azul violeta
5. amarillo, violeta
6. amarillo verdoso, rojo violeta

B. 1. alta intensidad
2. baja intensidad

C. 1.–2. Las respuestas variarán.

Lección 4

A. Las selecciones de los colores variarán, pero deben corresponder con la selección de *cálido* o *fresco*.
1. cálido
2. fresco
3. cálido
4. cálido
5. fresco

B. 1. verde y azul
2. anaranjado
3. rojo
4. violeta
5. cálido
6. amarillo
7. fresco

Lección 5

A. ritmo visual; motivo; patrón; ritmo regular; ritmo alterno; ritmo aleatorio; ritmo progresivo; ritmo continuo

Lección 6

A. 1. color cálido; color fresco
2. esquema del color
3. esquema monocromático del color
4. colores complementarios; esquema análogo del color
5. ritmo visual

B. 1. Un esquema monocromático del color incluye valores de un solo color. Un esquema análogo del color incluye varios colores relacionados, por ejemplo amarillo verdoso, verde y azul.
2. Un esquema monocromático del color basado en el color azul incluiría tintes y sombras de azul.

UNIDAD 3

Lección 1

A. 1. Una rosquita es espacio positivo. El espacio alrededor de la rosquita y el hoyo de la rosquita son espacios negativos.
2. El árbol es espacio positivo. El espacio alrededor del árbol es espacio negativo.

B. Los estudiantes deben encerrar en un círculo el primer diseño del vaso y las caras.

C. 1. c
2. a
3. d
4. b
Los estudiantes deben encerrar en un círculo la definición en la oración 3.

Lección 2

A. 1. falso
2. verdadero
3. falso
4. verdadero
5. verdadero

B. Las respuestas pueden variar, pero podrían incluir lo siguiente:
Inverso progresivo: cuando un objeto comienza como un objeto o forma y lentamente cambia a otro objeto o forma.
Teselado: un tipo de figura inversa que cambia rápidamente y encaja como un rompecabezas.

Lección 3
A. 1. visual
2. táctil
3. visual
4. táctil
5. visual
B. Las respuestas variarán.
C. textura imitada o textura visual. (La textura imitada es una clase de textura visual.)

Lección 4
A. 1. Los estudiantes deben dibujar un cuadrado.
2. Los estudiantes deben dibujar un círculo.
3. Los estudiantes deben dibujar un triángulo.
4. Los estudiantes deben dibujar un círculo o un rectángulo.
B. Las respuestas variarán, pero deben describir dos técnicas de sombreado tales como plumear, sombrear con líneas que se entrecruzan, puntear o mezclar.

Lección 5
A. El arquitecto planifica el puente y supervisa su construcción.
B. 1. arquitecto
2. arquitectura
C. arte: bellos en forma y proporción; basadas en ciertas ideas de proporción, escala y belleza.

Lección 6
1. forma
2. mate
3. brillante
4. áspera
5. armadura
6. suave
7. táctil

UNIDAD 4

Lección 1
A. 1. porción
2. pedazo o parte
3. Las oraciones variarán, pero deben enfocar la proporción corporal como una relación en el tamaño de las partes del cuerpo.
B. Los estudiantes deben encerrar en un círculo las oraciones 2 y 3.

Lección 2
A. proporción; escala; escala; escala
B. 1. escala real
2. escala irreal
3. escala real
C. Los estudiantes deben hacer dos dibujos de los dos objetos iguales, en uno mostrando los objetos en escala real y en otro en escala irreal.

Lección 3
A. 1. proporciones faciales
2. eje central
3. proporciones de perfil
B. 1. facial
2. facial
3. de perfil
4. de perfil
5. facial
6. facial

Lección 4
A. 1. Ambas palabras describen un incremento en tamaño o cantidad.
2. La nariz se hace más grande de lo que realmente es para destacarla.
3. Tú dirías que tienes más habilidad de la que realmente tienes.
B. Los estudiantes deben marcar los enunciados 1, 4 y 5.
C. Los estudiantes deben hacer el dibujo de una cara con ojos extraordinariamente grandes.

Lección 5
A. resultan de un cambio en la manera que algo realment es; agrandas; cambias en muchas formas diferentes (los ejemplos de distorsión pueden variar.)
B. 1.–3. Los dibujos variarán.

Lección 6
A. razón; proporciones corporales; escala
B. 1. La razón que expresa el tamaño apropiado de arriba a abajo de la forma humana.
2. 1:1.6 ó 1 a 1.6
3. a, c

UNIDAD 5

Lección 1

A. 1. Equilibrio
   2. Equilibrio formal
   3. Simetría
B. 1. equilibrio formal
   2. simetría
   3. equilibrio
   4. eje central
   5. grabado en relieve

Lección 2

A. Las respuestas variarán, pero pueden incluir las siguientes:
   1. Simetría significa que las partes de un objeto son imágenes idénticas. Asimetría significa que las partes no son imágenes idénticas.
   2. En equilibrio formal, los elementos semejantes en cada lado tienen el mismo peso visual. En equilibrio informal, existen elementos *desiguales* en cada lado, pero se equilibran entre sí.
B. Las respuestas variarán, pero pueden incluir la siguiente:
   Existe más espacio negativo alrededor de los triángulos más pequeños, lo cual ayuda a equilibrar el espacio positivo más grande que ocupa el triángulo grande.

Lección 3

A. 1. radar
   2. un rostro humano; una hoja de arce
   3. eje central
B. punto central; círculo; mitades; eje; imágenes idénticas
C. Los estudiantes deben encerrar en un círculo el dólar de arena y el plato de porcelana.

Lección 4

A. 1. c
   2. a
   3. b
B. 1. Cada árbol es un poco más pequeño que el que está más cerca del espectador. Debido a que los objetos más distantes se ven más pequeños, vemos la fila de árboles en el dibujo como si se extendiera más y más lejos.
   2. La casa cubre parte del granero y silo, y así es como aparecería ante nosotros. También, la casa es más baja y más larga, esto hace que se vea más cercana al espectador que el granero y el silo.

Lección 5

A. 1. punto de fuga
   2. perspectiva
B. 1. línea del horizonte
   2. perspectiva
   3. perspectiva lineal
C. Los estudiantes deben rotular la línea del horizonte y el punto de fuga.

Lección 6

A. Las descripciones variarán, pero deben mencionar las partes de una bicicleta que serían obvias al verlas de frente (manubrios, guardafango frontal, llanta delantera); desde un lado (manubrios, llantas delantera y posterior, guardafangos, estructura y asiento); desde arriba (manubrios, estructura, asiento, guardafango delantero y posterior); y desde atrás (asiento, guardafango posterior, llanta posterior).
B. Las respuestas variarán, pero deben incluir que el artista puede aprender más acerca de la estructura y los detalles de un objeto a través de la observación directa.
C. 1. frontal
   2. aéreo
   3. posterior
   4. lateral
   El objeto es un auto.

UNIDAD 6

Lección 1

A. destaque; ubicación; contraste; aislamiento
B. Los estudiantes deben enumerar varios tipos y texturas de tela y pega, o aguja e hilo.
C. 1. destacar
   2. aislamiento
   3. aplicación
   4. contraste

Lección 2

A. Las respuestas variarán, pero deben indicar que ambas palabras se relacionan con la visión y con lo que es central en una actividad o un objeto.
B. 1. urdimbre
   2. urdimbre
   3. trama
   4. urdimbre
   5. trama
C. destacar; punto focal

ART CONNECTIONS
LEVEL 5

Lección 3

A. Las respuestas variarán, pero deben incluir lo siguiente:
1. Puede contener artículos acerca de una variedad de temas.
2. Contiene muchos tipos y estilos diferentes de ropa.
3. Si haces muchas cosas en tu vida, no te aburrirás.

B. 1. variado; que contiene muchas cosas diferentes
2. multicolor; que tiene varios colores
3. serie; diferentes

C. Se usa variedad para crear o sea causar contraste.

Lección 4

A. 1–4. Las respuestas variarán, pero deben incluir:
1. En ambos se pegan pedazos de diferentes materiales a una superficie.
2. Ambos son tridimensionales.
3. Las partes corresponden de tal forma que parecen formar parte de un todo.
4. Ambos ubican elementos que corresponden; los elementos en la música son sonidos y los elementos en el arte son imágenes visuales.

B. Los dibujos y las explicaciones variarán.

Lección 5

A. 1. unidad; tacha uniforme
2. variedad; tacha universitario
3. armonía; tacha armazón

B. 1. variedad
2. armonía
3. unidad

Lección 6

Las respuestas variarán, pero deben incluir lo siguiente:

Puente colgante: Los cables, las cabillas, las columnas y el camino son figuras muy diferentes hechas de diferentes materiales, pero han sido muy bien combinadas. Esta bella y funcional combinación de materiales y figuras permite que la gente cruce de un lado del río al otro.

Pulsera: Los eslabones, la placa con el nombre y el broche están unidos de una manera agradable y eso funciona bien para sostener la joya en la muñeca del individuo. Todos los diferentes elementos tienen una cualidad redondeada, como la forma redondeada de la muñeca.